That Noise!

by Penny Dolan and Gerald Kelley

W
FRANKLIN WATTS
LONDON•SYDNEY

First published in 2011 by
Franklin Watts
338 Euston Road
London
NW1 3BH

Franklin Watts Australia
Level 17/207 Kent Street
Sydney
NSW 2000

A CIP catalogue record for this book is available
from the British Library.

ISBN 978 0 7496 9473 9 (hbk)
ISBN 978 0 7496 9479 1 (pbk)

Series Editor: Jackie Hamley
Series Advisor: Catherine Glavina
Series Designer: Peter Scoulding

Printed in China

Franklin Watts is a divison of
Hachette Children's Books,
an Hachette UK company.
www.hachette.co.uk

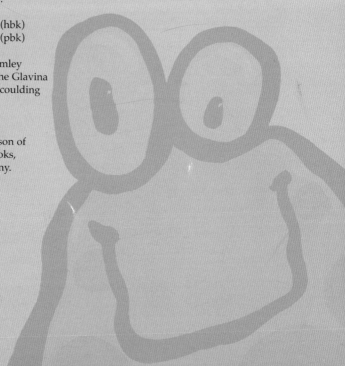

TO ALISON LYON
AND DRUMS AGOGO
– P. D.

Everything was quiet and peaceful.

Then Joe started clicking his fingers. Clickety click!

Josh started tapping
the table. Tappity tap!

Tara hit her chair.

Bang-banga! Bang-banga!

Tomas made sounds with his mouth. Tuck-tucka! Tuck-tucka!

Ravi patted his knees.
Pat-pata! Pat-pata!

Gloria shook her pencil case. Rattle rattle! Rattle rattle!

"Hmm, hmm!" hummed Jay.

"Hmm, hmm!" hummed Jenna.

And they clapped their
hands together.
Patapat! Patapat!

12

"Who," said Mr Edwards, "is making all that noise?"

Mr Edwards looked
at everyone.

"Right, all of you! I want to see you later!"

So later they all waited
outside Mr Edwards' room.

Mr Edwards

"Come in," said Mr
Edwards. He was smiling!

Mr Edwards

Everyone stared.
There were so
many drums!

Mr Edwards

"Want to learn?"
asked Mr Edwards.

They played those drums
and bells and shakers.

They played until the sound was just right.

Then they played in front of everyone!

They played the small drums. "Pat, patta! Pat, patta!"

They played the big drums. "Dum a dum, dum a dum!"

They made those iron
bells ring. "Ding ding!
Ding ding ding!"

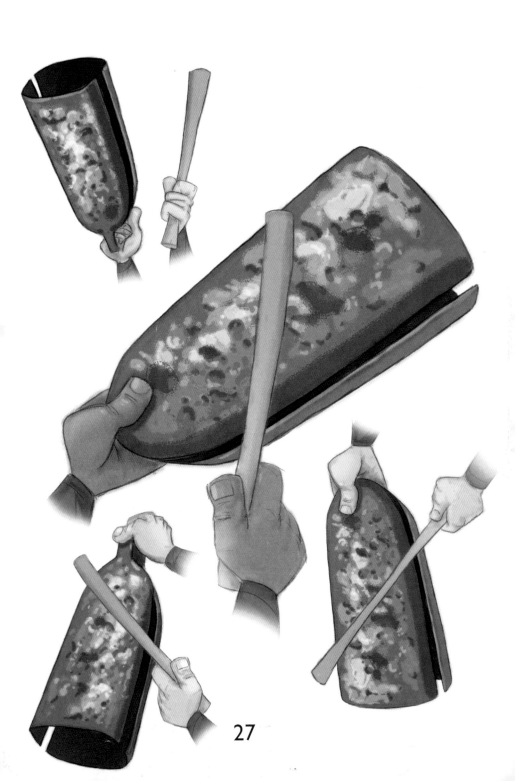

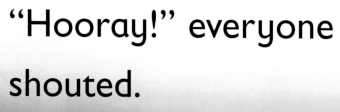

"Hooray!" everyone shouted.

"We just **love** that noise!"

Puzzle 1

Put these pictures in the correct order.
Now tell the story in your own words.
How short can you make the story?

Puzzle 2

angry   pleased

proud

excited   happy

miserable

Choose the words which best describe each character. Can you think of any more? Pretend to be one of the characters!

Answers

Puzzle 1

The correct order is:

1d, 2e, 3a, 4f, 5b, 6c

Puzzle 2

Mr Edwards The correct words are pleased, proud.

The incorrect word is angry.

Ravi The correct words are excited, happy.

The incorrect word is miserable.

Look out for more Leapfrog stories:

The Little Star
ISBN 978 0 7496 3833 7

Mary and the Fairy
ISBN 978 0 7496 9142 4

Jack's Party
ISBN 978 0 7496 4389 8

Pippa and Poppa
ISBN 978 0 7496 9140 0

The Bossy Cockerel
ISBN 978 0 7496 9141 7

The Best Snowman
ISBN 978 0 7496 9143 1

Big Bad Blob
ISBN 978 0 7496 7092 4*
ISBN 978 0 7496 7796 1

Cara's Breakfast
ISBN 978 0 7496 7797 8

Croc's Tooth
ISBN 978 0 7496 7799 2

The Magic Word
ISBN 978 0 7496 7800 5

Tim's Tent
ISBN 978 0 7496 7801 2

Why Not?
ISBN 978 0 7496 7798 5

Sticky Vickie
ISBN 978 0 7496 7986 6

Handyman Doug
ISBN 978 0 7496 7987 3

Billy and the Wizard
ISBN 978 0 7496 7985 9

Sam's Spots
ISBN 978 0 7496 7984 2

Bill's Baggy Trousers
ISBN 978 0 7496 3829 0

Bill's Bouncy Shoes
ISBN 978 0 7496 7990 3

Bill's Scary Backpack
ISBN 978 0 7496 9458 6*
ISBN 978 0 7496 9468 5

Little Joe's Big Race
ISBN 978 0 7496 3832 0

Little Joe's Balloon Race
ISBN 978 0 7496 7989 7

Little Joe's Boat Race
ISBN 978 0 7496 9457 9*
ISBN 978 0 7496 9467 8

Felix on the Move
ISBN 978 0 7496 4387 4

Felix and the Kitten
ISBN 978 0 7496 7988 0

Felix Takes the Blame
ISBN 978 0 7496 9456 2*
ISBN 978 0 7496 9466 1

The Cheeky Monkey
ISBN 978 0 7496 3830 6

Cheeky Monkey on Holiday
ISBN 978 0 7496 7991 0

Cheeky Monkey's Treasure Hunt
ISBN 978 0 7496 9455 5*
ISBN 978 0 7496 9465 4

For details of all our titles go to: www.franklinwatts.co.uk

*hardback